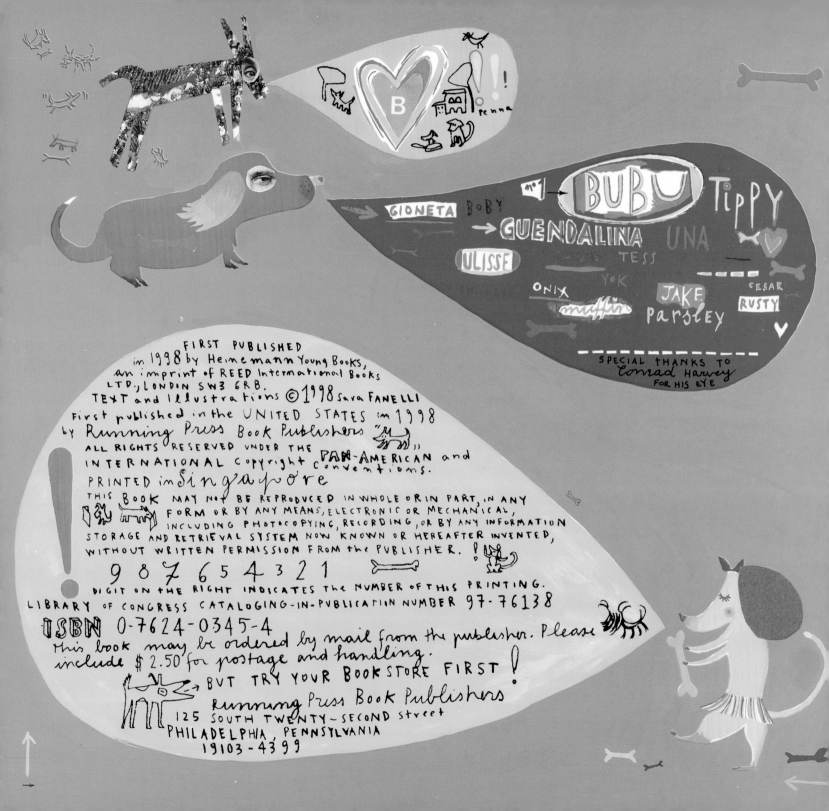

FIRST PUBLISHED in 1998 by Heinemann Young Books, an imprint of REED International Books LTD., LONDON SW3 6RB.

TEXT and Illustrations ©1998 Sara FANELLI

First published in the UNITED STATES in 1998 by Running Press Book Publishers

ALL RIGHTS RESERVED UNDER THE PAN-AMERICAN and INTERNATIONAL Copyright Conventions.

PRINTED in Singapore

9 8 7 6 5 4 3 2 1

DIGIT ON THE RIGHT INDICATES THE NUMBER OF THIS PRINTING.

LIBRARY OF CONGRESS CATALOGING-IN-PUBLICATION NUMBER 97-76138

ISBN 0-7624-0345-4

This book may be ordered by mail from the publisher. Please include $2.50 for postage and handling.

BUT TRY YOUR BOOKSTORE FIRST!

Running Press Book Publishers
125 SOUTH TWENTY-SECOND Street
PHILADELPHIA, PENNSYLVANIA
19103-4399

SPECIAL THANKS TO Conrad Harvey FOR HIS EYE

SARA  FaneLLi

the

DoGGY

BooK

RUNNING PRESS
PHILADELPHIA · LONDON

the **WORLD** ①

French

Italian

كلب

MOROCCAN

ädbí

JAPANESE

ほね

k i o c
a i o n a
m m i o a
n o

DOGS

Greyhound

BULLDOG (French)

As the saying goes:
dogs are like to their mistresses
PLATO

Mastiff

Basset

and MASTERS

1
2

Poodle

Afghan

Ears

1. RETRIEVER

2. COCKER SPANIEL

3. BULL terrier

4. CHOW CHOW

5. BASSET HOUND

6. MALTESE terrier

7. TIBETAN APSO

8. FRENCH BULLDOG

9. AFGHAN HOUND

10. BELGIAN SHEPHERD DOG

11. CAIRN terrier

12. CHIHUAHUA

13. TERRIER

14. BOXER

Tails

1. AFGHAN HOUND

2. YORKSHIRE Terrier

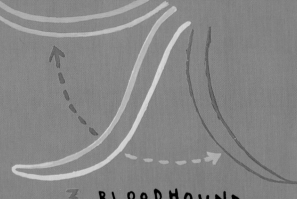

3. BLOODHOUND

4. BASENJI

5. BULL Terrier

6. CAIRN terrier

7. BEAGLE

8. ROTTWEILER

9. HUSKY

10. TIBETAN APSO

dogs smile with their tails

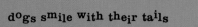

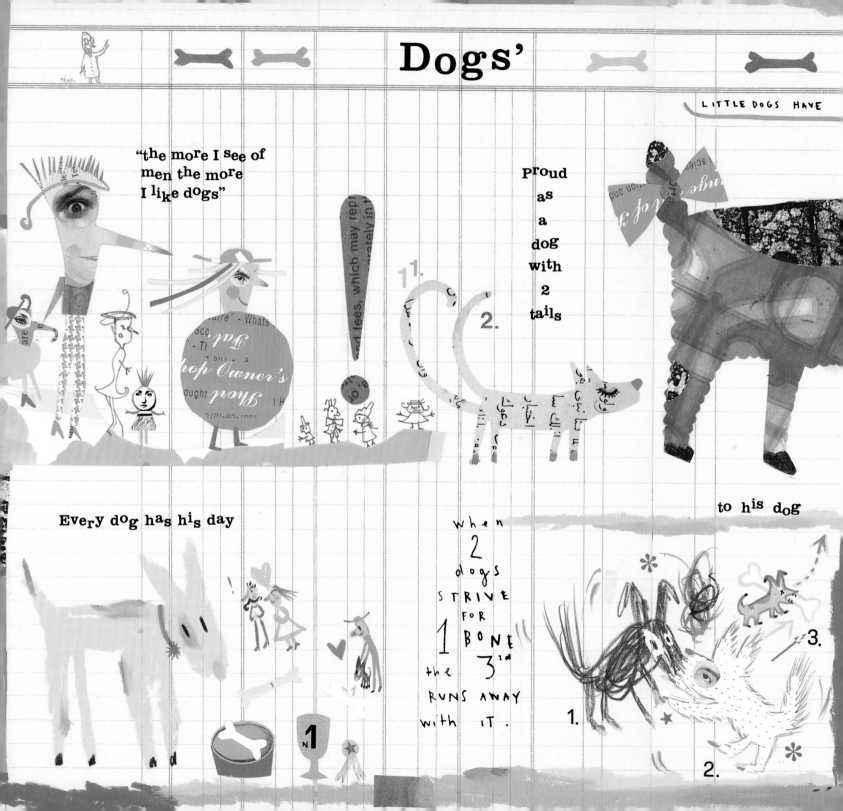

LITTLE DOGS HAVE

"the more I see of men the more I like dogs"

Proud as a dog with 2 tails

11.

2.

Every dog has his day

to his dog

when 2 dogs STRIVE FOR 1 BONE the 3rd RUNS AWAY WITH IT.

1 BONE

N1

1.

2.

3.

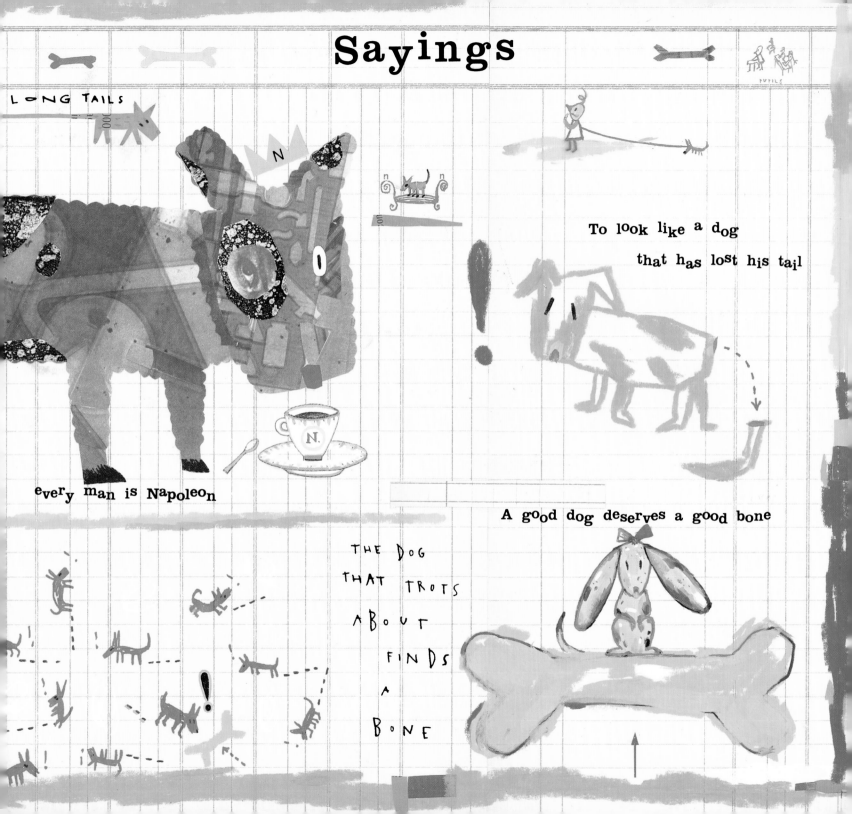

LONG TAILS

N

every man is Napoleon

To look like a dog
that has lost his tail

A good dog deserves a good bone

THE DOG
THAT TROTS
ABOUT
FINDS
A
BONE

DOGS'

Newspaper dog

Racing dog

Musician

A dog for company

Sheep dog

A dog to fetch your slippers

Sleigh dog

PROFESSIONS

Guard dog

Space dog

Circus dogs

Guide dog

Truffle hunter

CIRCUS

HOLY DOG

GUARDIAN ANGEL

FOR several hundred years DOGS BRED AT the Monastery of the GREAT ST. BERNARD PASS in Switzerland were TRAINED to RESCUE TRAVELERS LOST in the MOUNTAINS.

St. Bernard

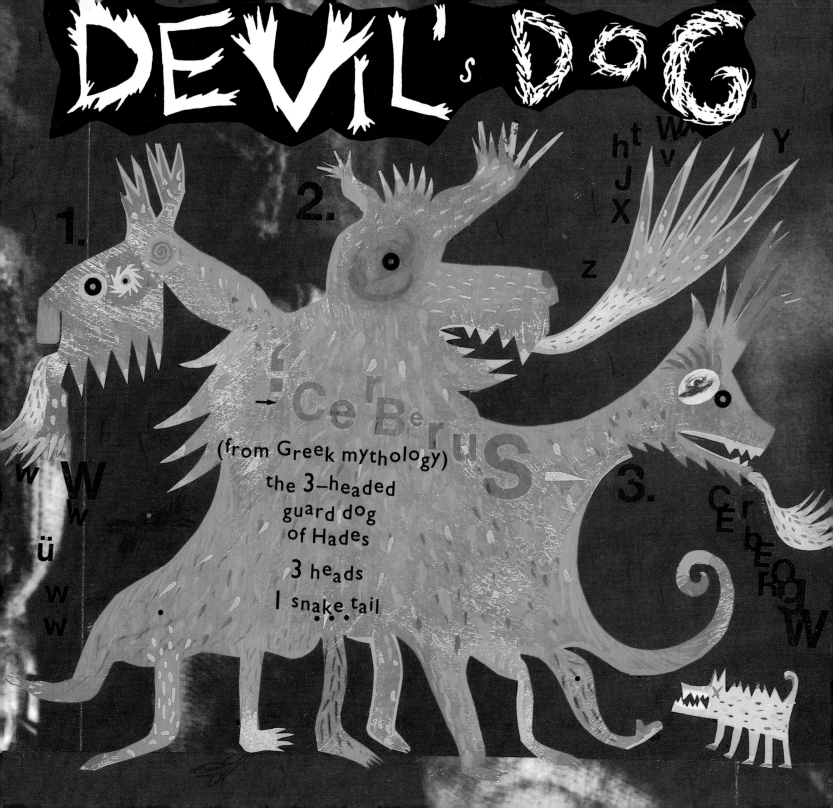

ACCESSORIES

POOCH PACIFIER
(ham bone
FLAVORED)

PLASTIC
TOYS

PET PORTRAITS

fifi

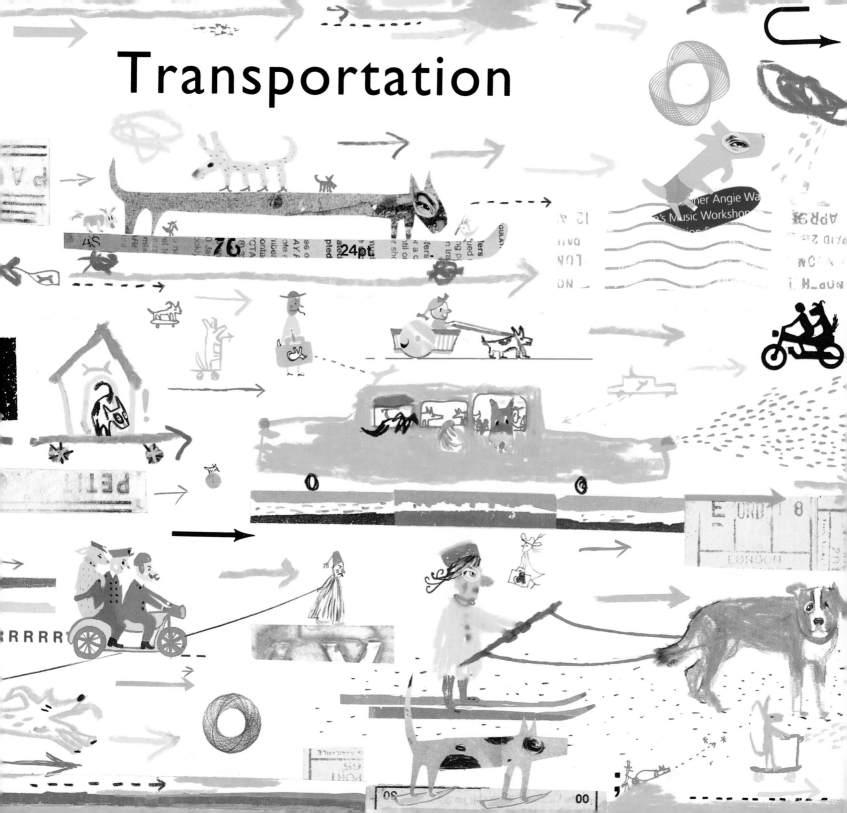

Transportation

THE MOST IMPORTANT
of ALL
IS THE DOG WHO GREETS YOU
EVERY DAY, WHO IS
ALWAYS HAPPY TO SEE YOU,
TO WHOM YOU CAN TELL
YOUR SECRETS, WITH WHOM
YOU CAN SWIM DURING HOT
SUMMERS AND GO FOR A
WALK IN A SPRING DAY.

MAKE YOUR OWN DOG!

1. —— TRACE DOG'S PARTS
2. ✂ CUT PARTS OUT OF CARDBOARD
3. PUNCH HOLES WHERE there is A Ⓐ MARK
4. USE 🖇 TO JOIN PARTS
5. MAKE YOUR DOG MOVE!

accessories

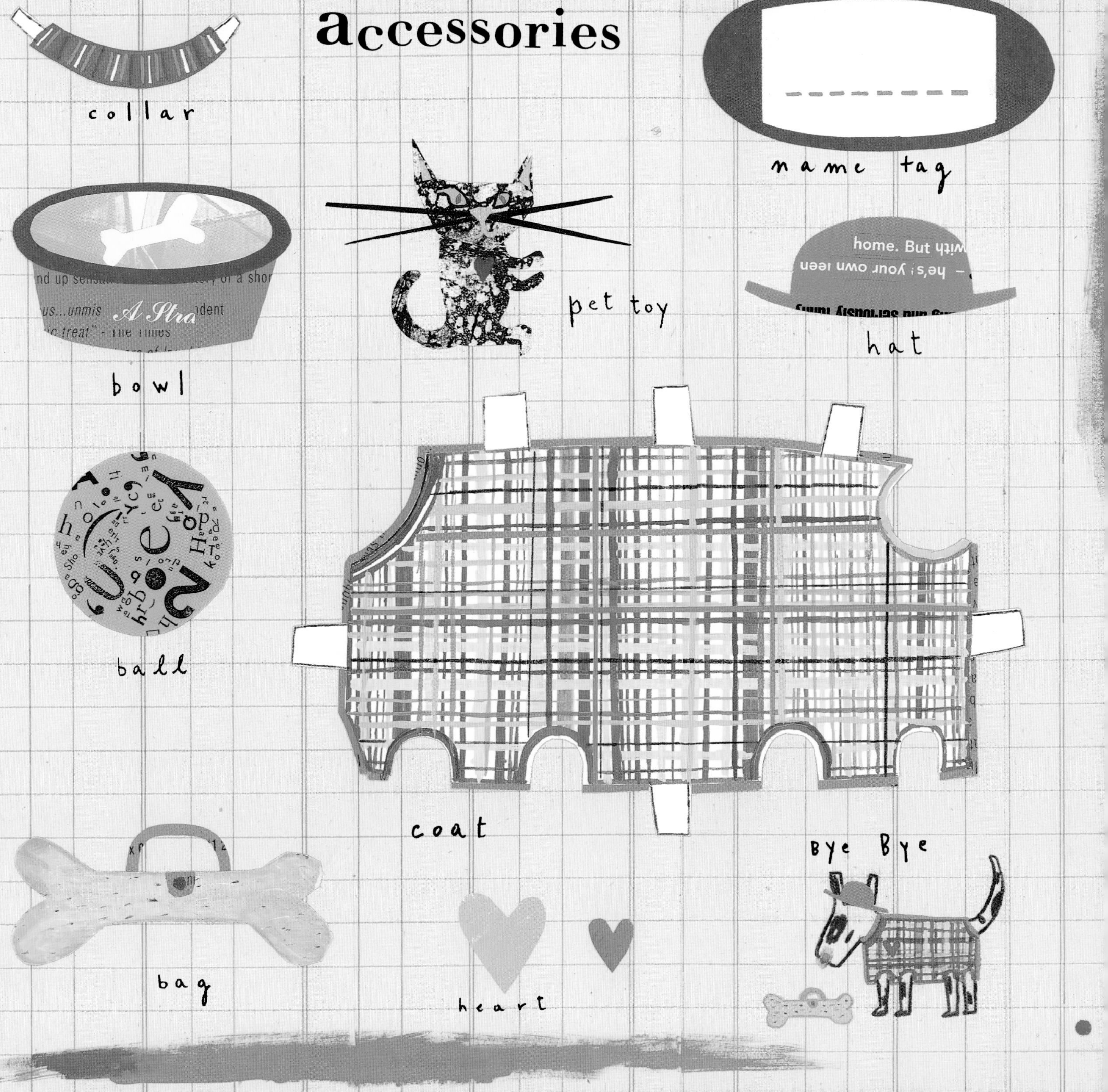

collar

name tag

bowl

pet toy

hat

ball

coat

bag

heart

Bye Bye

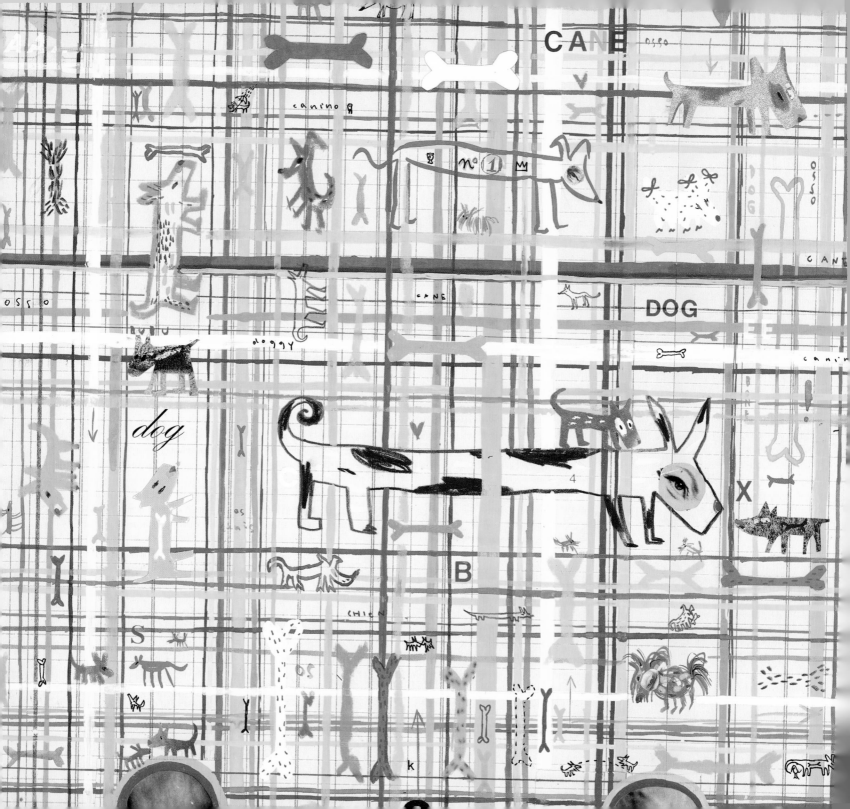